THE WOOD IS SWEET

JOHN CLARE
The Wood is Sweet

Poems for young readers chosen by
David Powell

Introduced by
Edmund Blunden

ILLUSTRATED BY JOHN O'CONNOR

THE BODLEY HEAD
LONDON SYDNEY
TORONTO

ISBN 0 370 01078 7
This collection © David Powell 1966
Foreword © The Bodley Head Ltd 1966
Illustrations © The Bodley Head Ltd 1966
Printed in Great Britain for
The Bodley Head Ltd
9 Bow Street, London WC2E 7AL
by Unwin Brothers Limited, Woking
This collection first published 1966
Reprinted 1971

He loved the brook's soft sound,
   The swallow swimming by,
He loved the daisy-covered ground,
   The cloud-bedappled sky.

The Peasant Poet

Acknowledgments

The poems in this selection have been taken from Professor J. W. Tibble's two-volume edition (Dent, 1935) and from Geoffrey Grigson's *Poems of John Clare's Madness* (Routledge and Kegan Paul, 1949).

In the absence of a definitive edition of Clare's poems, these two works have also been the main source for the present text. Reference has also been made to J. W. and Anne Tibble's *John Clare Selected Poems* (Dent, 1965). In some of Clare's later poems emendations have been made on the basis of W. F. Knight's asylum transcripts which now form part of the Clare Collection in the Northampton Public Library.

Thanks are also due to Mr Edmund Blunden for his kindly interest during the preparation of this book, and to Mr Eric Robinson for permission to print certain poems that were first published after Clare's death.

DAVID POWELL

About John Clare

John Clare was born at Helpston, Northamptonshire, in 1793 in circumstances more humble than those of Burns. He early developed a love of nature and rural life, and of books and ballad-collecting. His first volume, *Poems Descriptive of Rural Life and Scenery*, was published in 1820, and was an immediate success. Clare visited London, was lionised, and met Charles Lamb.

The story of the years that followed Clare's triumph was one of desperate struggle, first at Helpston, and then at Northborough (a village three miles distant where he moved in 1832), to earn a livelihood for his wife and family, and of stubborn refusal to accept the loss of recognition that came to him with the undeserved failure of his subsequent volumes. His actions grew stranger and more unpredictable, his suffering more pronounced, and in 1837, his friends fearing for his health, he was removed to the High Beech Asylum in Epping Forest.

Improved in health, he escaped four years later. After a few months at home he relapsed into his former condition, and was taken to the General Lunatic Asylum at Northampton, now St Andrew's Hospital, where he spent the last twenty-two years of his life. Here he composed some of his best poetry. During much of the time he was allowed to wander the town and the surrounding country at will, and was often seen in his favourite seat in the portico of All Saints' Church. He died on the 20th of May, 1864, and was buried at Helpston.

DAVID POWELL

Introduction by

EDMUND BLUNDEN

That John Clare through all his experiences, which were as varied (and as alarming often) as a long life can offer, succeeded in saving from corruption the spirit of childhood in himself, his readers well know. Once or twice he seems to apologise for this unalterable characteristic of his: 'I feel as ill becomes a man.' But in the end he was not in doubt over the rightness of his remaining in many things a child at heart. It was something like this view of the world through all vicissitude that attracted him so charmingly to Elia as a man and an essayist, and one may believe attracted Charles Lamb to him.

After all, as the biography of Clare by John and Anne Tibble published some ten years ago shows clearly, this famous 'Northamptonshire Peasant' had a great deal in his childhood to compensate for obvious disadvantages of serious importance. Earlier writers on Clare's home and setting, in the village he hailed in verse of the student sort as 'humble Helpstone', made enough fuss about the squalor and oafishness of the place, especially the actual birthplace. We might be influenced by the skilful method of his ardent biographer, Frederick Martin, in 1865, evolving at once a village of gloom and mud and a hovel scarcely rising to pig-stye rank, had not the truth become much easier to find out. To see with Clare's innocent eye may still not be so simple as to take a photograph in Woodgate, Helpston.

Again and again when he was confined miles from there as insane, Clare wrote of the wonderful childhood that he had had. It is remarkable that a later poet who had been in boyhood Clare's neighbour in the village of Barnack also

9

left us an impression of the rich and great times that he had then known. This was Charles Kingsley. His testimony is a stirring passage of prose, chiefly expressing the plenitude of wild life in the Clare country about the time when Clare was writing his greatest studies of it all in verse. The later poems to which I have referred are such as 'My Early Home', duly included in the present anthology:

> Here sparrows build upon the trees,
>   And stock-dove builds her nest;
> The leaves are winnowed by the breeze
>   Into a calmer rest;
> The blackcap's song was very sweet,
>   That used the rose to kiss;
> It made the paradise complete:
>   My early home was this.

The paradise! Clare was, he says without demur, a Wordsworthian, and yet we need not think he is in his own verses imitating the ever-sounding mystical thought 'Heaven lies about us in our infancy'. Not even when he uses the words:

> A stranger to the thoughts of men,
> He felt his boyish limbs agen
> Revelling in all the glee
> Of life's first fairy infancy.

In fact his is an earthly paradise, if we allow for some fairies in our woods or his. His fancies mingled with his discoveries, while he was still a boy, and he had his share of visionary moods when 'Heaven looked downward to the mind', and he 'shaped clouds to angels and beheld them smile'. But the chief thing was his gift of seeing and in every way recognising the amazing fulness of life round his early home. He speaks of sweet nature's book with its multitude of pages, beloved scenes, moments, sensations, 'favourite things'.

We may be forced to reflect while we delight in all that universe of nature beautifully and tunefully depicted by Clare that the child in England today has not such a concourse of happy secrets waiting to be found as soon as he or she closes the door and hastens along the lane. The lament for much that has been lost is not mere sentimental fooling; even in Clare's village or White's Selborne nature has been impoverished, and, besides, old customs and alluring legends and ballads and knowledges have partly died away. Yet much remains for the young mind to meet and fresh senses to welcome. Many of our poets may be described as inspirations in these encounters, so happy has their observation been, so song-like their recording of this green earth and its drama. Clare, on the whole, was more 'one with nature' than any of them, and his daily fairyland is 'one continuous song'.

He wrote a number of poems deliberately 'for the amusement of children', the word 'amusement' having once a little deeper meaning than now, and perhaps those pieces are not those which children most enjoy. It is a pity, or at least I feel that it is, not to have one or two details about some of the Asylum poems, as they have so long been called. His great love for children and reverence for childhood even when his own situation was so unhappy yielded several lyrics which have appealed to the child world of these later days. Did some small visitors ask him to write occasionally? I should like to think that a bold request by one of these led to the composition of, for instance, 'Little Trotty Wagtail'. This poem seems to have been, all the same, 'deliberate', for it is not one of Clare's elaborate descriptions; it is more like a 'note' on a wagtail in a terse Bewick tailpiece.

In years long past, before the recent widespread response to John Clare's genius, my mother was accustomed to share 'Little Trotty Wagtail' with the clients in her Infants' School, and she would say with pleasure how they liked it, every time. It is one of Clare's truly rhythmic poems, folk-tunes in language, which mark him as a metrist of an unusual kind—

in England at least—and it may well be that his ability with his fiddle and his practice of getting down on paper the odd tunes he heard at inns and fairs contributed much to these lyrical ballads.

In the following pages children—of all ages—can come into the kingdom of the child-like Clare, and even when he speaks of the ways of nature and the inhabitants of the countryside beyond our immediate acquaintance with them we may feel at home. For him beauty certainly was truth, and there was plenty for his watchful, grateful poetic self to receive. It is with particular regard that I view Mr Powell's selection of the poems. He is one who has already done faithful service in another way for Clare, and for those who 'sue to know Clare better', he has indeed, through his access to many manuscripts and books and relics of the poet, been living in his spiritual company for years past. The sensitive quality in the choice of poems will be quickly acknowledged by all who look into the book, town dwellers equally with those who may still notice Clare's birds, flowers, trees, weathers and village children at their threshold or near it.

EDMUND BLUNDEN

Contents

' . . . *In every season of the varied year*'

NATURE

There is a charm in Nature felt and seen
In every season of the varied year.
In Winter's frost, in Spring's reviving green,
    'Tis everywhere.

In foreign lands how beautiful the sight
Over a thousand mountains of snow spray,
With nought of green but mountains pale as light
    And all the way.

The Spring's green herbage full of flowers
And fields where lives the lark mid greener grain—
We love and worship them in April hours,
    Then wish again

That Spring with all her joys would longer last;
But Summer with young buds is left to choose
And brings once more in memory of the past
    Flowers of all hues.

Then autumn red and yellow quickly pass
Like broods of nestling birds upon the wing,
Till all is gone and nothing but the grass
    Remembers Spring.

The wind, the shower, the drapery of the sky
When day cools over meadows into dun,
And clouds in gold and crimson glories lie
    In set of sun,

A globe of fire and as a table round,
Then wastes to half, still shutting out the day,
Till the curved rim drops quickly in the ground,
    And all is grey.

FLOWERS

Ere yet the year is one month old,
 In spite of frost and wind and snow,
Bare-bosomed to the quaking cold,
 Spring's little selfsown flowers will blow;
And ever kin to early hours
 Peep aconites in cups of gold,
With frilled leaves muffled round their flowers
 Like tender maidens shunning cold;

And then as winter's parting pledge,
 Like true love in his crabbed reign,
The violets 'neath the naked hedge
 Peep thro' the rustling leaves again,
Soon as from off the thicket's moss
 The sunshine clears the doubting snow,
And the o'erjoyed and neighing horse
 Can find a patch of green to blow.

Like jewels brought by early hours,
 These little littered blossoms come;
Like wanderers from fairy bowers,
 They smile and gladly find a home;
And on the threshold of the spring,
 Like timid children out of doors,
They lie and wait the birds to sing,
 And laugh upon the splashy moors,

In April's smiling-frowning weather,
 Like younkers to a holiday,
The young flowers bud in troops together
 To wait the feast of merry May;
In sunny nooks and shelter nurst,
 Buds all their early blooms display,
Where sunbeams show their faces first
 And make when there the longest stay.

What charms does Nature at the spring put on,
    When hedges unperceiv'd get stain'd in green;
When even moss, that gathers on the stone,
    Crown'd with its little knobs of flowers is seen;
And every road and lane, through field and glen,
    Triumphant boasts a garden of its own.
In spite of nipping sheep, and hungry cow,
    The little daisy finds a place to blow:
And where old Winter leaves her splashy slough,
    The lady-smocks will not disdain to grow;
And dandelions like to suns will bloom,
    Aside some bank or hillock creeping low;
Though each too often meets a hasty doom
    From trampling clowns, who heed not where they go.

FIRST SIGHT OF SPRING

The hazel-blooms, in threads of crimson hue,
   Peep through the swelling buds and look for spring
Ere yet a whitethorn leaf appears in view,
   Or March finds throstles pleased enough to sing.
To the old touchwood tree woodpeckers cling
A moment, and their harsh-toned notes renew;
   In happier mood, the stock-dove claps his wing;
The squirrel sputters up the powdered oak,
   With tail cocked o'er his head and ears erect,
Startled to hear the woodman's understroke;
   And with the courage which his fears collect,
He hisses fierce half malice and half glee,
Leaping from branch to branch about the tree,
   In winter's foliage, moss and lichens, deckt.

HOME PICTURES IN MAY

The sunshine bathes in clouds of many hues
And morning's feet are gemmed with early dews;
Warm daffodils about the garden beds
Peep through their pale slim leaves their golden heads,
Sweet earthly suns of spring; the gosling broods,
In coats of sunny green, about the road
Waddle in ecstasy; and in rich moods
The old hen leads her flickering chicks abroad,
Oft scuttling 'neath her wings to see the kite
Hang wavering o'er them in the spring's blue light.
The sparrows round their new nests chirp with glee
And sweet the robin spring's young luxury shares,
Tootling its song in feathery gooseberry tree
While watching worms the gardener's spade unbares.

JUNE

Now summer is in flower, and Nature's hum
Is never silent round her bounteous bloom;
Insects, as small as dust, have never done
With glitt'ring dance, and reeling in the sun;
And green wood-fly, and blossom-haunting bee,
Are never weary of their melody.
Round field and hedge, flowers in full glory twine,
Large bindweed bells, wild hop, and streak'd woodbine,
That lift athirst their slender-throated flowers,
Agape for dew-falls, and for honey showers;
These o'er each bush in sweet disorder run,
And spread their wild hues to the sultry sun.
The mottled spider, at eve's leisure, weaves
His webs of silken lace on twigs and leaves,
Which every morning meet the poet's eye,
Like fairies' dew-wet dresses hung to dry . . .

from *The Shepherd's Calendar*

SUMMER MOODS

I love at eventide to walk alone,
   Down narrow lanes o'erhung with dewy thorn,
Where from the long grass underneath, the snail
   Jet-black creeps out and sprouts his timid horn.
I love to muse o'er meadows newly mown,
   Where withering grass perfumes the sultry air;
Where bees search round with sad and weary drone
   In vain for flowers that bloomed but newly there;
While in the juicy corn, the hidden quail
   Cries 'Wet my foot!' and, hid as thoughts unborn,
The fairy-like and seldom seen landrail
   Utters 'Craik, craik,' like voices underground:
Right glad to meet the evening's dewy veil,
   And see the light fade into glooms around.

THE WOODLAND STILE

When one's been walking in the open plain,
  Where the sun ne'er winks his eye, 'tis sweet
    awhile
To meet the shadows of a narrow lane
  Or quiet arbour of a woodland stile,
To sit and hear the little bees complain
  Among the woodbine blossoms o'er their toil,
And the hoarse murmurs of the distant swain,
  Driving his horses o'er the sunburnt soil;
While shadows hide me and leaves entertain
  My fancies with their freaks around my seat,
Dancing and whispering with the wooing wind
  Like lovers o'er their secrets; while the heat
Glimmers without and can no passage find
  To hurt the joys which rest so longed to meet.

FIELD THOUGHTS

Field thoughts to me are happiness and joy,
When I can lie upon the pleasant grass
Or track some little path and so employ
My mind in trifles, pausing as I pass
O'er little wild-flower clumps by nothing nurst
But dews and sunshine and impartial rain;
And welcomely to quench my summer thirst
I bend me by the flaggy dyke to gain
Dewberries, so delicious to the taste;
And then I wind the flag-fringed meadow lake
And mark the pike plunge with unusual haste
Through water-weeds and many a circle make,
While bursts of happiness from heaven fall;
There all have hopes; here fields are free for all.

SUMMER IMAGES

AN EXTRACT

I love at early morn, from new-mown swath,
   To see the startled frog his route pursue,
And mark while, leaping o'er the dripping path,
   His bright sides scatter dew;
And early lark that from its bustle flies
   To hail his matin new;
      And watch him to the skies:

And note on hedgerow baulks, in moisture sprent,
   The jetty snail creep from the mossy thorn,
With earnest heed and tremulous intent,
   Frail brother of the morn,
That from the tiny bents and misted leaves
   Withdraws his timid horn,
      And fearful vision weaves:

Or swallow heed on smoke-tanned chimney-top,
   Wont to be first unsealing morning's eye,
Ere yet the bee hath gleaned one wayward drop
   Of honey on his thigh;
To see him seek morn's airy couch to sing,
   Until the golden sky
      Bepaint his russet wing:

And sawning boy by tanning corn espy,
   With clapping noise to startle birds away,
And hear him bawl to every passer-by
   To know the hour of day;
And see the uncradled breeze, refreshed and strong,
   With waking blossoms play,
      And breathe Aeolian song.

I love the south-west wind, or low or loud,
  And not the less when sudden drops of rain
Moisten my pallid cheek from ebon cloud,
  Threatening soft showers again,
That over lands new ploughed and meadow
    grounds,
  Summer's sweet breath unchain,
    And wake harmonious sounds.

Rich music breathes in summer's every sound;
  And in her harmony of varied greens,
Woods, meadows, hedgerows, cornfields, all around
  Much beauty intervenes,
Filling with harmony the ear and eye;
  While o'er the mingling scenes
    Far spreads the laughing sky.

And wind-enamoured aspen—mark the leaves
  Turn up their silver lining to the sun,
And list! the brustling noise, that oft deceives,
  And makes the sheep-boy run:
The sound so mimics fast-approaching showers,
  He thinks the rain begun,
    And hastes to sheltering bowers . . .

THE WATER LILIES

The water lilies, white and yellow flowers,
  How beautiful they are upon the lake!
I've stood and looked upon the place for hours,
  And thought how fine a garden they would make.
The pleasant leaves upon the water float;
  The dragon-fly would come and stay for hours,
And when the water pushed the pleasure boat,
  Would find a safer place among the flowers.
They lay like Pleasure in a quiet place,
  Close where the moor-hen loved her nest to
    make,—
They lay like Beauty with a smiling face,
  And I have called them 'Ladies of the Lake!'
I've brought the longest pole and stood for hours,
And tried for years, before I got those flowers!

Black grows the southern sky, betokening rain,
    And humming hive-bees homeward hurry by:
They feel the change; so let us shun the grain,
    And take the broad road while our feet are dry.
Ay, there some dropples moistened on my face,
    And pattered on my hat—'tis coming nigh!
Let's look about, and find a sheltering place.
    The little things around, like you and I,
Are hurrying through the grass to shun the shower.
    Here stoops an ash-tree—hark! the wind gets
      high,
But never mind; this ivy, for an hour,
    Rain as it may, will keep us dryly here:
That little wren knows well his sheltering bower,
    Nor leaves his dry house though we come so near.

SONG

The rain is come in misty showers,
  The landscape lies in shrouds;
Patches of sunshine like to flowers
  Fall down between the clouds
And gild the earth, elsewhere so cold,
With shreds like flowers of purest gold.

And now it sweeps along the hills
  Just like a falling cloud,
The cornfields into silence stills
  Where misty moisture shrouds;
And now a darker cloud sweeps o'er,
The rain drops faster than before.

The cattle graze along the ground,
  The lark she wets her wings
And chatters as she whirls around,
  Then to the wet corn sings,
And hides upon her twitchy nest,
Refreshed, with wet and speckled breast.

And I the calm delight embrace
  To walk along the fields
And feel the raindrops in my face
  That sweetest pleasure yields;
They come from heaven and there the Free
Sends down his blessings upon me.

I love to walk in summer shower
  When the rain falls gently down,
I love to walk a leisure hour
  A distance from the town,
To see the drops on bushes hing
And blackbirds prune a dabbled wing.

FIR-WOOD

The fir-trees taper into twigs and wear
The rich blue-green of summer all the year,
Softening the roughest tempest almost calm
And offering shelter ever still and warm
To the small path that travels underneath,
Where loudest winds—almost as summer's breath—
Scarce fan the weed that lingers green below
When others out of doors are lost in snow.
And sweet the music trembles on the ear
As the wind suthers through each tiny spear,
Makeshifts for leaves; and yet, so rich they show,
Winter is almost summer where they grow.

THE AUTUMN ROBIN

AN EXTRACT

Sweet little bird in russet coat,
   The livery of the closing year,
I love thy lonely plaintive note
   And tiny whispering song to hear.
While on the stile or garden seat
   I sit to watch the falling leaves,
The song thy little joys repeat
   My loneliness relieves . . .

AUTUMN

I love the fitful gust that shakes
The casement all the day,
And from the mossy elm-tree takes
The faded leaf away,
Twirling it by the window-pane
With thousand others down the lane.

I love to see the shaking twig
Dance till the shut of eve,
The sparrow on the cottage rig,
Whose chirp would make believe
That spring was just now flirting by
In summer's lap with flowers to lie.

I love to see the cottage smoke
Curl upwards through the naked trees,
The pigeons nestled round the cote
On dull November days like these;
The cock upon the dunghill crowing,
The mill-sails on the heath a-going.

The feather from the raven's breast
Falls on the stubble lea,
The acorns near the old crow's nest
Fall pattering down the tree;
The grunting pigs, that wait for all,
Scramble and hurry where they fall.

NOVEMBER

The shepherds almost wonder where they dwell,
And the old dog for his right journey stares:
The path leads somewhere, but they cannot tell,
And neighbour meets with neighbour unawares.
The maiden passes close beside her cow,
And wanders on, and thinks her far away;
The ploughman goes unseen behind his plough
And seems to lose his horses half the day.
The lazy mist creeps on in journey slow;
The maidens shout and wonder where they go;
So dull and dark are the November days.
The lazy mist high up the evening curled,
And now the morn quite hides in smoke and haze;
The place we occupy seems all the world.

SNOWSTORM

What a night! The wind howls, hisses, and but
  stops
To howl more loud, while the snow volley keeps
Incessant batter at the window-pane,
Making our comforts feel as sweet again;
And in the morning, when the tempest drops,
At every cottage door mountainous heaps
Of snow lie drifted, that all entrance stops
Until the besom and the shovel gain
The path, and leave a wall on either side.
The shepherd, rambling valleys white and wide,
With new sensations his old memory fills,
When hedges left at night, no more descried,
Are turned to one white sweep of curving hills,
And trees turned bushes half their bodies hide.

WINTER SNOWSTORM

Winter is come in earnest, and the snow,
In dazzling splendour crumping underfoot,
Spreads a white world all calm, and where we go
By hedge or wood trees shine from top to root
In feathered foliage, flashing light and shade
In strangest contrast; fancy's pliant eye
Delighted sees a vast romance displayed
And fairy halls descended from the sky;
The smallest twig its snowy burthen bears,
And woods o'erhead the dullest eyes engage
To shape strange things where arch and pillar
    bears
A roof of grains fantastic, arched, and high;
A little shed beside the spinney wears
The grotesque semblance of an hermitage.

'*I love the gentle dawning*'

BREAK OF DAY

The lark he rises early,
　And the ploughman goes away
Before it's morning fairly
　At the guessing break of day;
The fields lie in the dawning,
　And the valley's hid in gold,
At the pleasant time of morning
　When the shepherd goes to fold.

The maiden laughs and hollos
　When she sees the feeding cows;
They switch their tails and follow
　When she can't get over sloughs;
I love the gentle dawning,
　And the valleys hid in gold,
At the pleasant time of morning
　When the shepherd goes to fold.

MORNING

The morning comes, the drops of dew
Hang on the grass and bushes too;
The sheep more eager bite the grass
Whose moisture gleams like drops of glass;
The heifer licks in grass and dew
That make her drink and fodder too.
The little bird his morn-song gives,
His breast wet with the dripping leaves,
Then stops abruptly just to fly
And catch the wakened butterfly,
That goes to sleep behind the flowers
Or backs of leaves from dews and showers.
The yellowhammer, haply blest,
Sits by the dyke upon her nest;
The long grass hides her from the day,
The water keeps the boys away.
The morning sun is round and red
As crimson curtains round a bed,
The dew-drops hang on barley horns
As beads the necklace thread adorns,
The dew-drops hang wheat-ears upon
Like golden drops against the sun,
Hedge-sparrows in the bush cry 'tweet',
O'er nests larks winnow in the wheat,
Till the sun turns gold and gets more high,
And paths are clean and grass gets dry,
And longest shadows pass away.
And brightness is the blaze of day.

NOON

The midday hour of twelve the clock counts o'er,
    A sultry stillness lulls the air asleep;
The very buzz of flies is heard no more,
    Nor faintest wrinkles o'er the waters creep.
Like one large sheet of glass the pool does shine,
    Reflecting in its face the burnt sunbeam:
The very fish their sturting play decline,
    Seeking the willow-shadows 'side the stream.
And, where the hawthorn branches o'er the pool,
    The little bird, forsaking song and nest,
Flutters on dripping twigs his limbs to cool,
    And splashes in the stream his burning breast.
Oh, free from thunder, for a sudden shower,
To cherish nature in this noonday hour!

EVENING SCHOOLBOYS

Hark to that happy shout!—the school-house door
  Is open thrown, and out the younkers teem;
Some run to leap-frog on the rushy moor,
  And others dabble in the shallow stream,
Catching young fish, and turning pebbles o'er
  For mussel-clams. Look in that mellow gleam,
Where the retiring sun, that rests the while,
  Streams through the broken hedge! How happy seem
Those friendly schoolboys leaning o'er the stile,
  Both reading in one book!—Anon a dream,
Rich with new joys, doth their young hearts beguile,
  And the book's pocketed right hastily.
Ah, happy boys! well may ye turn and smile,
  When joys are yours that never cost a sigh.

CROWS CROWD CROAKING

Crows crowd croaking overhead,
Hastening to the woods to bed.
Cooing sits the lonely dove,
Calling home her absent love.
With 'Kirchup! kirchup!' 'mong the
　　wheats,
Partridge distant partridge greets . . .

Bats flit by in hood and cowl;
Through the barn-hole pops the owl;
From the hedge, in drowsy hum,
Heedless buzzing beetles bum,
Haunting every bushy place,
Flopping in the labourer's face . . .

from Summer Evening

RECOLLECTIONS
AFTER AN EVENING WALK

Just as the even-bell rang, we set out
To wander the fields and the meadows about;
And the first thing we mark'd that was lovely to view
Was the sun hung on nothing, just bidding adieu:
He seem'd like a ball of pure gold in the west,
In a cloud like a mountain blue, dropping to rest;
The skies all around him were ting'd with his rays,
And the trees at a distance seem'd all on a blaze,
Till, lower and lower, he sank from our sight,
And the blue mist came creeping with silence and night.
The woodman then ceas'd with his hatchet to hack,
And bent away home with his kid on his back;
The mower, too, lapt up his scythe from our sight,
And put on his jacket, and bid us good night;
The thresher once lumping, we heard him no more,
He left his barn-dust, and had shut up his door;
The shepherd had told all his sheep in his pen,
And humming his song, sought his cottage agen:
But the sweetest of all seeming music to me
Were the songs of the clumsy brown-beetle and bee;
The one was seen hast'ning away to his hive,
The other was just from his sleeping alive—
'Gainst our hats he kept knocking as if he'd no eyes,
And when batter'd down he was puzzled to rise.
The little gay moth, too, was lovely to view,
A-dancing with lily-white wings in the dew;
He whisk'd o'er the water-pudge flirting and airy,
And perch'd on the down-headed grass like a fairy.
And there came the snail from his shell peeping out,
As fearful and cautious as thieves on the rout;
The sly jumping frog, too, had ventur'd to tramp,

And the glow-worm had just 'gun to light up his lamp;
To sip of the dew the worm peep'd from his den,
But dreading our footsteps soon vanish'd agen:
And numbers of creatures appear'd in our sight,
That live in the silence and sweetness of night,
Climbing up the tall grasses or scaling the bough,
But these were all nameless, unnotic'd till now.
And then we wound round 'neath the brook's willow row,
And look'd at the clouds that kept passing below;
The moon's image too, in the brook we could see't,
As if 'twas the other world under our feet;
And we listen'd well pleas'd at the guggles and groans
The water made passing the pebbles and stones.
And then we turn'd up by the rut-rifted lane,
And sought for our cot and the village again;
For night gather'd round, and shut all from the eye,
And a black sultry cloud crept all over the sky;
The dew on the bush, soon as touch'd it would drop,
And the grass 'neath our feet was as wet as a mop:
And, as to the town we approach'd very fast,
The bat even popp'd in our face as he past;
And the crickets sang loud as we went by the house,
And by the barn-side we saw many a mouse
Quirking round for the kernels that, litter'd about,
Were shook from the straw which the thresher hurl'd out.
And then we came up to our cottage once more,
And shut out the night-dew, and lock'd up the door;
The dog bark'd a welcome, well-pleas'd at our sight,
And the owl o'er our cot flew, and whoop'd a 'good night.'

CLIFFORD HILL

The river rambles like a snake
    Along the meadow green,
  And loud the noise the mill-wheels make
    I' summer time at e'en;
And there as swift the waters pass,
    So runs the life of man,
I sit me down upon the grass,
    These beauties for to scan.

'Tis summer's day and dewy eve
    And sweet the sun sinks low,
I smile, and yet my heart will grieve
    To see the waters flow,
To see the flags that look so green,
    The sungilt waves so bright.
I wander here this lovely e'en
    In wonder and delight.

The firs look dark on Clifford Hill,
    The river bright below,
All foamed beneath the water-mill,
    While beauteous flowers do blow.
'Tis here I'd wander morn and night
    With fondly gazing eye,
To see the sunny golden light
    Go down in yonder sky.

Yes, dearly do these scenes I love,
    And dear that firclad hill;
There all secure does build the dove,
    While click-clack goes the mill.
And now in Nature's sweet repose
    I leave this spot awhile;
The bee is buried in the rose,
    And man gone from his toil.

EVENING PRIMROSE

When once the sun sinks in the west,
And dew-drops pearl the evening's breast,
Almost as pale as moonbeams are,
Or its companionable star,
The evening primrose opes anew
Its delicate blossoms to the dew;
And shunning, hermit-like, the light,
Wastes its fair bloom upon the night;
Who, blindfold to its fond caresses,
Knows not the beauty he possesses.
Thus it blooms on till night is by;
When day looks out with open eye,
'Bashed at the gaze it cannot shun,
It faints, and withers, and is done.

'Joyful are the thoughts of home'

THE WOOD-CUTTER'S NIGHT SONG

Welcome, red and roundy sun,
   Dropping lowly in the west;
Now my hard day's work is done,
   I'm as happy as the best.

Joyful are the thoughts of home,
   Now I'm ready for my chair,
So, till morrow-morning's come,
   Bill and mittens, lie ye there!

Though to leave your pretty song,
   Little birds, it gives me pain,
Yet to-morrow is not long,
   Then I'm with you all again.

If I stop, and stand about,
   Well I know how things will be,
Judy will be looking out
   Every now and then for me.

So fare ye well! and hold your tongues,
   Sing no more until I come;
They're not worthy of your songs
   That never care to drop a crumb.

All day long I love the oaks,
   But, at nights, yon little cot,
Where I see the chimney smokes,
   Is by far the prettiest spot.

Wife and children all are there,
   To revive with pleasant looks,
Table ready set, and chair,
   Supper hanging on the hooks.

Soon as ever I get in,
 When my faggot down I fling,
Little prattlers they begin
 Teasing me to talk and sing.

Welcome, red and roundy sun,
 Dropping lowly in the west;
Now my hard day's work is done,
 I'm as happy as the best.

Joyful are the thoughts of home,
 Now I'm ready for my chair,
So, till morrow-morning's come,
 Bill and mittens, lie ye there!

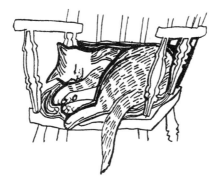

PROPOSALS FOR BUILDING A COTTAGE

Beside a runnel build my shed,
    With stubbles cover'd o'er;
Let broad oaks o'er its chimney spread,
    And grass-plats grace the door.

The door may open with a string,
    So that it closes tight;
And locks would be a wanted thing,
    To keep out thieves at night.

A little garden, not too fine,
    Inclose with painted pales;
And woodbines, round the cot to twine,
    Pin to the wall with nails.

Let hazels grow, and spindling sedge,
    Bent bowering overhead;
Dig old man's beard from woodland hedge,
    To twine a summer shade.

Beside the threshold sods provide,
    And build a summer seat;
Plant sweetbrier bushes by its side,
    And flowers that blossom sweet.

I love the sparrows' ways to watch
    Upon the cotters' sheds,
So here and there pull out the thatch,
    That they may hide their heads.

And as the sweeping swallows stop
    Their flights along the green,
Leave holes within the chimney-top
    To paste their nest between.

Stick shelves and cupboards round the hut,
 In all the holes and nooks;
Nor in the corner fail to put
 A cupboard for the books.

Along the floor some sand I'll sift,
 To make it fit to live in;
And then I'll thank ye for the gift,
 As something worth the giving.

LABOUR'S LEISURE

Oh, for the feelings and the careless health
That found me toiling in the fields, the joy
I felt at eve with not a wish for wealth,
When, labour done and in the hedge put by
My delving spade, I homeward used to hie
With thoughts of books I often read by stealth
Beneath the blackthorn clumps at dinner-hour;
It urged my weary feet with eager speed
To hasten home where winter fire did shower
Scant light, now felt as beautiful indeed,
Where bending o'er my knees I used to read
With earnest heed all books that had the power
To give me joy in most delicious ways
And rest my spirits after weary days.

MY EARLY HOME

Here sparrows build upon the trees,
  And stock-dove builds her nest;
The leaves are winnowed by the breeze
  Into a calmer rest;
The blackcap's song was very sweet,
  That used the rose to kiss;
It made the paradise complete:
  My early home was this.

The redbreast from the sweetbrier bush
  Dropt down to pick the worm;
On the horse-chestnut sang the thrush,
  O'er the home where I was born;
The dew-morn, like a shower of pearls,
  Fell o'er this 'bower of bliss',
And on the bench sat boys and girls:
  My early home was this.

The old house stooped just like a cave,
  Thatched o'er with mosses green;
Winter around the walls would rave,
  But all was calm within;
The trees they were as green agen,
  Where bees the flowers would kiss,
But flowers and trees seemed sweeter then:
  My early home was this.

'. . . the birds how busy now!'

BIRDS' NESTS

How fresh the air, the birds how busy now!
In every walk if I but peep I find
Nests newly made or finished all and lined
With hair and thistledown, and in the bough
Of little hawthorn, huddled up in green,
The leaves still thickening as the spring gets age,
The pink's, quite round and snug and closely laid,
And linnet's of materials loose and rough;
And still hedge-sparrow, moping in the shade
Near the hedge-bottom, weaves of homely stuff,
Dead grass and mosses green, an hermitage,
For secrecy and shelter rightly made;
And beautiful it is to walk beside
The lanes and hedges where their homes abide.

THE SKYLARK

The rolls and harrows lie at rest beside
The battered road; and spreading far and wide
Above the russet clods, the corn is seen
Sprouting its spiry points of tender green,
Where squats the hare, to terrors wide awake,
Like some brown clod the harrows failed to break.
Opening their golden caskets to the sun,
The buttercups make schoolboys eager run,
To see who shall be first to pluck the prize—
Up from their hurry, see, the skylark flies,
And o'er her half-formed nest, with happy wings
Winnows the air, till in the cloud she sings,
Then hangs a dust-spot in the sunny skies,
And drops, and drops, till in her nest she lies,
Which they unheeded passed—not dreaming then
That birds which flew so high would drop agen
To nests upon the ground, which anything
May come at to destroy. Had they the wing
Like such a bird, themselves would be too proud,
And build on nothing but a passing cloud!
As free from danger as the heavens are free
From pain and toil, there would they build and be,
And sail about the world to scenes unheard
Of and unseen—Oh, were they but a bird!
So think they, while they listen to its song,
And smile and fancy and so pass along;
While its low nest, moist with the dews of morn,
Lies safely, with the leveret, in the corn.

EARLY NIGHTINGALE

When first we hear the shy-come nightingales,
They seem to mutter o'er their songs in fear,
And, climb we e'er so soft the spinney rails,
All stops as if no bird was anywhere.
The kindled bushes with the young leaves thin
Let curious eyes to search a long way in,
Until impatience cannot see or hear
The hidden music; gets but little way
Upon the path—when up the songs begin,
Full loud a moment and then low again.
But when a day or two confirms her stay
Boldly she sings and loud for half the day;
And soon the village brings the woodman's tale
Of having heard the new-come nightingale.

THE YELLOWHAMMER

When shall I see the whitethorn leaves agen,
  And yellowhammers gathering the dry bents
By the dyke side, on stilly moor or fen,
  Feathered with love and nature's good intents?
Rude is the nest this architect invents,
  Rural the place, with cart-ruts by dyke side.
Dead grass, horsehair, and downy-headed bents
  Tied to dead thistles—she doth well provide,
Close to a hill of ants where cowslips bloom
And shed o'er meadows far their sweet perfume.
  In early spring, when winds blow chilly cold,
The yellowhammer, trailing grass, will come
To fix a place and choose an early home,
  With yellow breast and head of solid gold.

THE CHIFF-CHAFF

See at yon flitting bird that flies
    Above the oak tree tops at play,
Uttering its restless melodies
    Of 'chipichap' throughout the day.

Its nest is built in little bush
    Scarcely a foot above the ground,
Or hid in clumps of sedge or rush
    In woods where they are rarely found.

Its nest is like an oven made
    With moss and leaves and bits of grass,
And all so nice and snugly laid
    That hands may spoil but not replace.

It enters by a little hole,
    Its inside is a feather bed
From yards and poultry hovels stole;
    Its eggs are small and spotted red.

And all the spring and all the May,
    If I forbore the gate to clap,
Down that wood-riding day by day
    We heard it singing 'chipichap',

And o'er the tree-tops saw it fly,
    Dancing about, a fairy thing,
But never yet could come so nigh
    To tell the colour of its wing.

The bushes they are dripping wet,
    Or we would seek its curious nest,
There oft in bushy places met,
    Where sedges mingle with the rest.

LITTLE TROTTY WAGTAIL

Little trotty wagtail, he went in the rain,
And tittering tottering sideways, he near got straight again,
He stooped to get a worm, and look'd up to catch a fly,
And then he flew away ere his feathers they were dry.

Little trotty wagtail, he waddled in the mud,
And left his little footmarks, trample where he would.
He waddled in the water-pudge, and waggle went his tail,
And chirrupt up his wings to dry upon the garden rail.

Little trotty wagtail, you nimble all about,
And in the dimpling water-pudge you waddle in and out,
Your home is nigh at hand, and in the warm pigsty,
So, little Master Wagtail, I'll bid you a good-bye.

THE SWALLOW

AN EXTRACT

Pretty swallow, once again
Come and pass me in the rain.
Pretty swallow, why so shy?
Pass again my window by . . .

Pretty little swallow, fly
Village doors and windows by,
Whisking o'er the garden pales
Where the blackbird finds the snails; . .

On yon low-thatched cottage stop,
In the sooty chimney pop,
Where thy wife and family
Every evening wait for thee.

QUAIL'S NEST

I wandered out one rainy day
  And heard a bird with merry joys
Cry 'wet my foot' for half the way;
  I stood and wondered at the noise,

When from my foot a bird did flee—
  The rain flew bouncing from her breast—
I wondered what the bird could be,
  And almost trampled on her nest.

The nest was full of eggs and round;
  I met a shepherd in the vales,
And stood to tell him what I found.
  He knew and said it was a quail's,

For he himself the nest had found,
  Among the wheat and on the green,
When going on his daily round,
  With eggs as many as fifteen.

Among the stranger birds they feed,
  Their summer flight is short and low;
There's very few know where they breed,
  And scarcely any where they go.

THE THRUSH'S NEST

Within a thick and spreading hawthorn bush
  That overhung a mole-hill large and round,
I heard from morn to morn a merry thrush
  Sing hymns to sunrise, and I drank the sound
With joy; and, often an intruding guest,
  I watched her secret toils from day to day—
How true she warped the moss to form a nest,
  And modelled it within with wood and clay;
And by and by, like heath-bells gilt with dew,
  There lay her shining eggs, as bright as flowers,
Ink-spotted over shells of greeny blue;
  And there I witnessed, in the sunny hours,
A brood of nature's minstrels chirp and fly,
Glad as that sunshine and the laughing sky.

THE RED ROBIN

Cock Robin he got a neat tippet at spring,
And he sat in a shed and heard other birds sing,
And he whistled a ballad as loud as he could,
And built him a nest of oak leaves by the wood,

And furnished it just as the celandine pressed
Like a bright burning blaze by the edge of its nest,
All glittering with sunshine and beautiful rays,
Like high polished brass, or the fire in a blaze;

Then sung a new song on the bend of the brere;
And so it kept singing the whole of the year.
Till cowslips and wild roses blossomed and died,
The red robin sung by the old spinney side.

THE SEDGE-BIRD'S NEST

Fixed in a whitethorn bush, its summer guest,
  So low e'en grass o'er-topped its tallest twig,
A sedge-bird built its little benty nest,
  Close by the meadow pool and wooden brig,
Where schoolboys every morn and eve did pass
  In robbing birds, and cunning, deeply skilled,
Searching each bush and taller clump of grass,
  Where'er was likelihood of bird to build:
Yet did she hide her habitation long,
  And keep her little brood from danger's eye,
Hidden as secret as a cricket's song,
    Till they, well-fledged, o'er widest pools could fly;
    Proving that Providence is often by,
To guard the simplest of her charge from wrong.

KINGFISHERS

Look where two splendid feathered things
   Sit on that grey and stretching bough,
That from the leaning willow hings
   Half o'er the gulling flood below.
Like foreign birds' their plumage shines
   In splendour's rich and varied hue;
The peacock's tail is scarce as fine—
   Rich-shaded, orange, green, and blue.

No finer birds are known to fly
   Than these gay-dressed kingfishers are,
Who live on fish and watch the fry
   Of minnows nimbly passing there;
And there they'll sit whole hours away
   In that same lone and watching spot,
And when they dart to seize their prey
   Drop down as sudden as a shot.

Sandmartin-like, they make a hole
   A steepy headlong bank beside,
As well as ever did the mole,
   And there their many eggs they hide.
And as is natural to their kind,
   Where mill-dam waters wildly foam,
Places more hard to reach than find
   They choose, a safe and quiet home.

Their hole a full arm's length is made,
   Turned at the last with sudden bend,
Where lots of fishes' bones are laid
   Close to the large and furthest end;
Their eggs are white as wrynecks' be
   And much about that middle size,
And boys oft skulk behind a tree
   To watch the old one where she flies,
And then pull out their knives in glee
   And delve in vain to reach the prize.

THE FENS

Among the tawny tasselled reed
The ducks and ducklings float and feed.
With head oft dabbing in the flood
They fish all day the weedy mud,
And tumbler-like are bobbing there,
Heels topsy-turvy in the air,
Then up and quack and down they go.
Heels over head again below.

The geese in troops come droving up,
Nibble the weeds, and take a sup;
And closely puzzled to agree,
Chatter like gossips over tea.
The gander with his scarlet nose
When strife's at height will interpose;
And, stretching neck to that and this,
With now a mutter, now a hiss,
A nibble at the feathers too,
A sort of 'pray be quiet, do',
And turning as the matter mends,
He stills them into mutual friends;
Then in a sort of triumph sings
And throws the water o'er his wings . . .

'These tiny loiterers . . .'

INSECTS

These tiny loiterers on the barley's beard,
And happy units of a numerous herd
Of playfellows, the laughing summer brings,
Mocking the sunshine in their glittering wings,
How merrily they creep, and run, and fly!
No kin they bear to labour's drudgery,
Smoothing the velvet of the pale hedge-rose;
And where they fly for dinner no one knows—
The dew-drops feed them not—they love the shine
Of noon, whose sun may bring them golden wine.
All day they're playing in their Sunday dress—
Till night goes sleep, and they can do no less;
Then, to the heath-bell's silken hood they fly,
And like to princes in their slumbers lie,
Secure from night, and dropping dews, and all,
In silken beds and roomy painted hall.
So merrily they spend their summer day,
Now in the cornfields, now the new-mown hay,
One almost fancies that such happy things,
With coloured hoods and richly burnished wings,
Are fairy folk, in splendid masquerade
Disguised, as if of mortal folk afraid,
Keeping their merry pranks a mystery still,
Lest glaring day should do their secrets ill.

CLOCK-A-CLAY

In the cowslip's peeps I lie,
Hidden from the buzzing fly,
While green grass beneath me lies,
Pearled wi' dew like fishes' eyes.
Here I lie, a clock-a-clay,
Waiting for the time o' day.

While grassy forests quake surprise,
And the wild wind sobs and sighs,
My gold home rocks as like to fall,
On its pillar green and tall;
When the pattering rain drives by
Clock-a-clay keeps warm and dry.

Day by day and night by night,
All the week I hide from sight;
In the cowslip's peeps I lie,
In rain and dew still warm and dry;
Day and night, and night and day,
Red, black-spotted clock-a-clay.

My home it shakes in wind and showers,
Pale green pillar top't wi' flowers,
Bending at the wild wind's breath,
Till I touch the grass beneath.
Here still I live, lone clock-a-clay,
Watching for the time of day.

THE LADYBIRD

Ladybird! Ladybird! Where art thou gone?
Ere the daisy was open or the rose it was spread
On the cabbage flower early thy scarlet wings shone,
I saw thee creep off to the tulip's bed.
Ladybird! Ladybird! Where art thou flown?
Thou wert here in the morning before the sun shone.

Just now up the bole o' the damson tree
You passed the gold lichen and got to the grey—
Ladybird! Ladybird! Where can you be?
You climb up the tulips and then fly away.
You crept up the flowers while I plucked them just now
And crept to the top and then flew from the flowers.
O sleep not so high as the damson tree bough,
But come from the dew i' the eldern tree bower.

Here's lavender trees that would hide a lone mouse
And lavender cotton wi' buttons o' gold,
And bushes o' lad's love as dry as a house,
Here's red pinks and daisies so sweet to behold.
Ladybird! Ladybird! Come to thy nest,
Thy gold bed's i' the rose o' the sweetbrier tree,
Wi' rose-coloured curtains to pleasure thee best;
Come, Ladybird, back to thy garden and me.

THE ANTS

What wonder strikes the curious, while he views
    The black ant's city, by a rotten tree
Or woodland bank! In ignorance we muse:
    Pausing, annoy'd, we know not what we see,
    Such government and thought there seem to be;
Some looking on, and urging some to toil,
    Dragging their loads of bent-stalks slavishly;
And what's more wonderful, when big loads foil
One ant or two to carry, quickly then
A swarm flock round to help their fellow-men.
    Surely they speak a language whisperingly,
Too fine for us to hear; and sure their ways
    Prove they have kings and laws, and that they be
Deformed remnants of the fairy-days.

THE HEDGEHOG

The hedgehog hides beneath the rotten hedge
And makes a great round nest of grass and sedge,
Or in a bush or in a hollow tree;
And many often stoop and say they see
Him roll and fill his prickles full of crabs
And creep away; and where the magpie dabs
His wing at muddy dyke, in aged root
He makes a nest and fills it full of fruit,
On the hedge-bottom hunts for crabs and sloes
And whistles like a cricket as he goes.
It rolls up like a ball or shapeless hog
When gipsies hunt it with their noisy dog;
I've seen it in their camps—they call it sweet,
Though black and bitter and unsavoury meat.

THE SQUIRREL'S NEST

One day, when all the woods were bare and blea,
I wandered out to take a pleasant walk
And saw a strange-formed nest on stoven tree
Where startled pigeon buzzed from bouncing hawk.
I wondered strangely what the nest could be
And thought besure it was some foreign bird,
So up I scrambled in the highest glee,
And my heart jumped at every thing that stirred.
'Twas oval-shaped; strange wonder filled my breast;
I hoped to catch the old one on her nest
When something bolted out—I turned to see—
And a brown squirrel pattered up the tree.
'Twas lined with moss and leaves, compact and strong;
I sluthered down and wondering went along.

MOUSE'S NEST

I found a ball of grass among the hay
And progged it as I passed and went away;
And when I looked I fancied something stirred,
And turned agen and hoped to catch the bird—
When out an old mouse bolted in the wheats
With all her young ones hanging at her teats;
She looked so odd and so grotesque to me,
I ran and wondered what the thing could be,
And pushed the knapweed bunches where I stood;
Then the mouse hurried from the craking brood.
The young ones squeaked, and as I went away
She found her nest again among the hay.
The water o'er the pebbles scarce could run
And broad old cesspools glittered in the sun.

THE WOOD IS SWEET

The wood is sweet—I love it well,
   In spending there my leisure hours,
To seek the snail its painted shell,
   And look about for curious flowers;
Or 'neath the hazel's leafy thatch,
   On a stulp or mossy ground,
Little squirrel's gambols watch,
   Dancing oak trees round and round . . .

              from *Recollections after a Ramble*

THE VIXEN

Among the taller wood with ivy hung,
The old fox plays and dances round her young.
She snuffs and barks if any passes by
And swings her tail and turns prepared to fly.
The horseman hurries by, she bolts to see,
And turns agen, from danger never free.
If any stands she runs among the poles
And barks and snaps and drives them in the holes.
The shepherd sees them and the boy goes by
And gets a stick and progs the hole to try.
They get all still and lie in safety sure,
And out again when everything's secure,
And start and snap at blackbirds bouncing by
To fight and catch the great white butterfly.

HARES AT PLAY

The birds are gone to bed, the cows are still,
And sheep lie panting on each old mole-hill;
And underneath the willow's grey-green bough,
Like toil a-resting, lies the fallow plough.
The timid hares throw daylight fears away
On the lane's road to dust and dance and play,
Then dabble in the grain by naught deterred
To lick the dew-fall from the barley's beard;
Then out they sturt again and round the hill
Like happy thoughts dance, squat, and loiter still,
Till milking maidens in the early morn
Jingle their yokes and sturt them in the corn;
Through well-known beaten paths each nimbling hare
Sturts quick as fear, and seeks its hidden lair.

BADGER

When midnight comes a host of dogs and men
Go out and track the badger to his den,
And put a sack within the hole, and lie
Till the old grunting badger passes by.
He comes and hears—they let the strongest loose.
The old fox hears the noise and drops the goose.
The poacher shoots and hurries from the cry,
And the old hare half wounded buzzes by.
They get a forkèd stick to bear him down
And clap the dogs and take him to the town,
And bait him all the day with many dogs,
And laugh and shout and fright the scampering hogs.
He runs along and bites at all he meets:
They shout and hollo down the noisy streets.

He turns about to face the loud uproar
And drives the rebels to their very door.
The frequent stone is hurled where'er they go;
When badgers fight, then every one's a foe.
The dogs are clapt and urged to join the fray;
The badger turns and drives them all away.
Though scarcely half as big, demure and small,
He fights with dogs for hours and beats them all.
The heavy mastiff, savage in the fray,
Lies down and licks his feet and turns away.
The bulldog knows his match and waxes cold,
The badger grins and never leaves his hold.
He drives the crowd and follows at their heels
And bites them through—the drunkard swears and reels.

The frighted women take the boys away,
The blackguard laughs and hurries on the fray.
He tries to reach the woods, an awkward race,
But sticks and cudgels quickly stop the chase.
He turns agen and drives the noisy crowd
And beats the many dogs in noises loud.
He drives away and beats them every one,
And then they loose them all and set them on.
He falls as dead and kicked by boys and men,
Then starts and grins and drives the crowd agen;
Till kicked and torn and beaten out he lies
And leaves his hold and cackles, groans, and dies.

'*Meet me in the green glen*'

MEET ME IN THE GREEN GLEN

Love, meet me in the green glen,
  Beside the tall elm-tree;
Where the sweetbrier smells so sweet agen,
  There come with me,
    Meet me in the green glen.

Meet me at the sunset
  Down in the green glen,
Where we've often met
  By hawthorn-tree and foxes' den,
    Meet me in the green glen.

Meet me by the sheep-pen,
  Where briers smell at e'en,
Meet me i' the green glen,
  Where whitethorn shades are green,
    Meet me in the green glen.

Meet me in the green glen,
  By sweetbrier bushes there;
Meet me by your own sen,
  Where the wild thyme blossoms fair.
    Meet me in the green glen.

Meet me by the sweetbrier,
  By the mole-hill swelling there,
When the west glows like a fire
  God's crimson bed is there.
    Meet me in the green glen.

EXPECTATION

A BALLAD

'Tis Saturday night, and my shepherd will come
  With a hallo and whistle for me;
Be clear, O ye skies, take your storm-burthens home,
  Let no rain drench our favourite tree.
For I fear by the things that are hopping about
  There's a sign of a storm coming on;
The frog looks as black as the toad that creeps out
  From under its hiding-stone.

The cat with her tail runneth round till she reels
  And the pigs race with mouthfuls of hay;
I sigh at the sight, I feel sick over meals,
  For I'm lone when my shepherd's away.
When dogs eat the grass it is sure to be rain,
  And our dog's in the orchard e'en now;
The swallows fly low, and my heart is in pain,
  While the flies even madden the cow.

The pigeons have moped on the cote the day long,
  And the hens went to roost before noon;
The blackbirds, long still, din the woods with their song,
  And they look upon showers as a boon,
While they keep their nest dry in the wet hazel-bush
  And moisten their black sooty wings;
Did they know but my sorrows they'd quickly be hush:
  Birds to make lovers happy should sing.

87

I've often leaned over the croft's mossy gate
  To listen birds singing at night,
While I for the sure-footed Rover did wait,
  And rich was my bosom's delight.
And sweet had it been now I'm waiting anew
  Till the black snail is out from the grain,
But the south's ruddy clouds they have turned black and
    blue,
  And the blackbirds are singing for rain.

The thrush 'Wivy wit wivy wit' t'other night
  Sung aloud in the old sallow bush,
And I called him a pert little urchin outright
  To sing 'Heavy wet'; and the thrush
Changed his note in a moment to 'Cheer up' and 'Cheer',
  And the clouds crept away from the sun,
Till my shepherd he came, and when thrushes I hear
  My heart with the music is won.

But the blackbird is rude and insulting, and now,
  The more the clouds blacken the sky,
The louder he sings from the green hazel bough,
  But he may be sad by and by.
For the cow-boy is stooping beneath the oak tree
  Whose branches hang down to the ground,
And beating his stick on the bushes to see
  If a bird startles out from the sound.

So silence is safety, and, bird, have a care,
  Or your song will your dwelling betray;
For yesterday morning I saw your nest there,
  But sung not to fright you away.
And now the boy's near you; well done, cunning bird,
  You have ceased and popt out t'other side;
Your nest it is safe, not a leaf has he stirred,
  And I have my shepherd descried.

SONG

O, WERT THOU IN THE STORM

O, wert thou in the storm,
  How I would shield thee!
To keep thee dry and warm,
  A camp I would build thee.

Though the clouds pour'd again,
  Not a drop should harm thee;
The music of wind and rain
  Rather should charm thee.

O, wert thou in the storm,
  A shed I would build thee,
To keep thee dry and warm,
  How I would shield thee!

The rain should not wet thee,
  Nor thunderclap harm thee.
By thy side I would set me,
  To comfort and warm thee.

I would sit by thy side, love,
  While the dread storm was over,
And the wings of an angel
  My charmer would cover.

BESSEY THE MILKMAID

How sweet the wind of evening comes through the ashtree
boughs,
How sweet the milkmaid's soothing voice is calling up her
cows.
The bat is wheeling round the oak, the white moth round
the thorn,
And the lark is dropping to her nest in the outside lands
of corn.
The blue haze deepens with the green, the sun sets in the
gap.
The blue left is the selfsame hue of Bessey's bonny cap,
As she sits singing to herself upon her milking stool,
Beneath the oaks and willows by the old pond in the cool.

O bonny is the milkmaid that sings beneath the shade,
O lovely is the wildrose cheek of the bonny milking maid.
Her eyes turn on the cowslips so lovely to behold,
She thinks them like her earrings, rich pendant drops of
gold.
The lilies of the valley, and you might fill a peck,
Are not so white as underneath her 'kerchief is her neck.
The daisies and the pileworts they make a garden show,
Where the maiden sits a-milking by the thorn tree white
as snow.

What time beneath its crimson bank the orange setting sun
Sinks in the world of spirits and leaves the earth in dun
The happy milking maiden with her well-scoured milking
pail
Goes tripping down the village street and singing down
the vale.
The pendant golden cowslips keep tapping at her gown,
She's minding where to set her feet and winna break them
down.
And I'll bestir myself, and my love I'll strive to hide,
And gang to meet the milking maid down our burn side.

SONG

The wind waves o'er the meadows green
  And shakes my own wild flowers
And shifts about the moving scene
  Like the life of summer hours;
The little bents with reedy head,
  The scarce-seen shapes of flowers,
All kink about like skeins of thread
  In these wind-shaken hours.

All stir and strife and life and bustle
  In everything around one sees,
The rushes whistle, sedges rustle,
  The grass is buzzing round like bees.
The butterflies are tossed about
  Like skiffs upon a stormy sea,
The bees are lost amid the rout
  And drop in green perplexity.

Wilt thou be mine, thou bonny lass?
  Thy drapery floats so gracefully;
We'll walk along the meadow grass,
  We'll stand beneath the willow-tree.
We'll mark the little reeling bee
  Along the grassy ocean rove,
Tossed like a little boat at sea,
  And interchange our vows of love.

SONG

I HID MY LOVE

I hid my love when young while I
Couldn't bear the buzzing of a fly;
I hid my love to my despite
Till I could not bear to look at light:
I dare not gaze upon her face
But left her memory in each place;
Where'er I saw a wild flower lie
I kissed and bade my love good-bye.

I met her in the greenest dells,
Where dew-drops pearl the wood bluebells;
The lost breeze kissed her bright blue eye,
The bee kissed and went singing by,
A sunbeam found a passage there,
A gold chain round her neck so fair;
As secret as the wild bee's song
She lay there all the summer long.

I hid my love in field and town
Till e'en the breeze would knock me down;
The bees seemed singing ballads o'er,
The fly's buzz turned a lion's roar;
And even silence found a tongue,
To haunt me all the summer long;
The riddle nature could not prove
Was nothing else but secret love.

Index of First Lines

Index of First Lines

95